SHIRE NATURAL HIST(

C000242451

THE
MANDARIN DUCK

CHRISTOPHER LEVER

CONTENTS

Cover: *A mandarin drake in full breeding plumage.*

Series editor: Jim Flegg.

Copyright © 1990 by Sir Christopher Lever, Bt. First published 1990.
Number 53 in the Shire Natural History series. ISBN 0 7478 0055 3.

Printed in Great Britain by C. I. Thomas & Sons (Haverfordwest) Ltd,
Press Buildings, Merlins Bridge, Haverfordwest, Dyfed SA61 1XF.

The mandarin duck

The mandarin duck *(Aix galericulata)* is a member of the family Anatidae — the swans, geese and ducks. Within this family of some 143 different species, which provides a microcosm of avian evolution, can be found many links between different genera, but also some genera whose relationships have for long perplexed ornithological taxonomists.

Swans, geese and ducks are characterised by having the front toes of the feet webbed for swimming (and in some species for diving), flat bills with special plates adapted for sieving out food items, and thick feathers with insulating down. They are mostly strong fliers, though in many cases not especially swift, and some, such as the mandarin and teal *(Anas crecca)*, because of their high wing area to weight ratio, are very manoeuvrable. Their flight feathers are moulted simultaneously after breeding, leaving them temporarily flightless. In many species the plumage of males differs markedly from that of females.

The Anatidae are mainly aquatic birds, ranging from standing waters to rushing torrents, from the open seas to high-altitude montane lakes, and from the marshes of the Arctic and sub-Arctic tundra (treeless plains) and taiga (park-like forests) to tropical and semi-tropical rainforest and cloudforest. They feed on animal and vegetable matter; the nest, which is normally situated on the ground or in a hole in a tree, is usually lined with down.

Mandarin are members of the tribe Cairinini (the perching ducks) and apart from the wood duck *(Aix sponsa)* of North America, which from time to time escapes from avicultural collections and has occasionally bred in the wild, have no close relations in Britain.

The mandarin drake possesses an amazing and bizarre plumage which makes him one of the most beautiful and striking ducks — indeed one of the most beautiful birds — in the world. He has a purple-green and copper-tinged crested head *(galericulata* means 'wearing a little wig' or 'cap'), a broad white eye stripe which extends from in front of the eye back along the side of the head through the crest, an orange-chestnut ruff of pointed feathers that hang down from his neck like side-whiskers, a glossy purple breast with three black and two white vertical stripes on either side, buffish flanks, white underparts, a greenish brown back, and a pair of magnificent golden-orange 'fans' or 'sails' which rise vertically on either side of his back, formed of greatly enlarged and expanded central tertial wing feathers; his bill is vermilion tipped with pink, his legs are orange-yellow, and the iris of his eyes is dark brown with a lemon-yellow outer ring.

The head, neck and crest of the female are a soft lilac-grey, with a small greyish ruff; the chin and throat are white, and a white spectacle stripe runs from around the eye into the crest at the nape of the neck; the upperparts are olive-brown with a greenish sheen, and the breast and sides are browny grey with rows of whitish oval spots; the wings and tail vary from pale brown to dark sepia; the eyes are brown, the legs brownish yellow, and the bill is greyish brown with a pale orange tip.

In summer, after breeding, the males of many species of ducks moult into a sombre 'eclipse' plumage in which, until they grow new feathers, they closely resemble the females and, because of the loss of their flight feathers, they become temporarily flightless. In eclipse plumage the mandarin drake can be distinguished from the duck by his reddish bill, yellower legs, less pronounced white markings around the eyes and at the base of the bill, a heavier crest, and a glossier plumage with browner mottling on the underparts.

In appearance, mandarin are fairly small, compact ducks, with a short bill, a large head, a thickish neck, and a long tail in relation to the size of the body; adult males measure between 41 and 49 cm (16-19 inches) in length and weigh some 560-670 grams (1¼-1½ pounds). They are thus rather larger than a teal.

Mandarin are believed to be monotypic (that is, no subspecies have so far been recognised, though birds from Korea may formerly have represented a distinct race, now lost due to introductions from Japan which have swamped the native population) and with the closely related and also monotypic North American wood or summer duck, known to aviculturists as the Carolina duck, are the sole representatives of the genus *Aix*. It has from time to time been conjectured that there may still be two subspecies of *galericulata* — an intriguing speculation which DNA 'fingerprinting' might help to resolve. Wood duck frequently occur and sometimes breed in the wild in Britain but are not yet on the official British and Irish list, to which the mandarin was admitted in 1971.

CHARACTERISTICS

Mandarin ducks are normally found on fresh water, including streams, rivers, ponds and lakes, in well wooded areas. They are usually secretive and shy but, if fed regularly, can become quite tame. They swim well, with the body high on the water and the tail often slightly raised. They seldom up-end and do not normally dive for food, though they will dive readily enough if injured or alarmed. On land they walk easily and frequently perch on low branches or the trunks and boughs of fallen trees. They rise easily from both land and water and are strong though not swift fliers, seldom ascending much higher than tree-top level. The wing area/weight ratio of mandarins is one of the highest of all the ducks and this, together with their proportionately long tails, gives them great aerial manoeuvrability, enabling them to jink easily among the branches of trees and either to make a normal feet-forward landing on water or to plunge gannet-like with half-closed wings to within a few feet of the surface before checking their descent. They are most often seen singly, in pairs or in small parties, though sometimes in large flocks. Because of their special habitat requirements, mandarins seldom mix with other species.

1. *A pair of mandarin at a nesting box in water.*

VOICE

Except during communal courtship and when disturbed or in flight, the mandarin is a relatively silent bird. The calls of the drake are mostly variations of a sharp rising whistle accompanied by a lower, snorting nasal sound. The four main calls, all involving whistles, given during communal courtship are summarised in Cramp and Simmons (1977): a basic courtship call consisting of a short 'prfruib' uttered especially at the start of communal courtship; a display-shake call, comprising a soft and melodious whirring whistle, 'fwwwww' and 'rrrrr' pronounced simultaneously; a double display-shake call, 'grik-zit', like a partially stifled sneeze, followed by a short sneeze-like whistle; and a burp call, consisting of a long drawn-out 'pffrrruuiehb'. The alarm call, on taking wing, is a shrill whistling 'uib', and the flight call a brief whistling and rather plaintive 'wriick' or 'hwick'.

The six main calls of the female are described in Cramp and Simmons: a coquette call — a loud sharp single 'kett' or 'ke', which can easily be mistaken for the 'kewk' call of a coot (Fulica atra), given as the principal component of the coquette display of communal courtship; an inciting call, consisting of a rapidly repeated and plaintive-sounding 'ack', uttered during inciting display; a clucking call, comprising a soft, often repeated, barely audible and twittering 'cluca-cluca-cluca'; a sibilant hissing, given when disturbed late on in incubation; a so-called 'exodus call', a soft, melodious encouraging note used by the female to entice the young from the nest-hole; and a deep throaty rolling 'rrr-r-ruck' distraction call to warn young and divert predators.

FOOD AND FEEDING

Although mandarins can be classed as omnivorous, they eat mainly vegetable matter, especially seeds and nuts, and some small animals such as insects and land snails. In Britain they feed largely on small invertebrates in spring, in summer on insects (especially Diptera) taken from aquatic plants, on amphibious bistort (Polygonum amphibium, commonly known as 'pink tooth-brush' waterweed) and on small amphibians; in autumn and winter they survive almost entirely on acorns, chestnuts (Castanea or Aesculus species) and beechmast (Fagus sylvaticum). The young eat mainly insects and larvae, as well as small fish and plant material.

Mandarin are nocturnal and diurnal feeders, both on land and in the water; in the latter they feed mainly at the margins but also dabble and, less frequently, up-end, but they seldom dive.

ROOSTING

After their last feed of the day, normally at dusk, mandarin preen before sleeping. Outside the breeding season they usually roost in small parties on rocks, logs or fallen trees in secluded locations in or near water. During the breeding season drakes normally roost by themselves in trees near the nesting site.

The mandarin in the Far East

The mandarin duck is a native of eastern Asia, where it is found mainly in China and Japan, inhabiting well established forests intersected by rivers, streams and lakes, seldom far from the coast. Here mandarins formerly bred from around 40°N on the Chinese mainland, principally in the Tung Ling (Eastern Tombs) Forest, previously the Imperial Hunting Grounds, north of Beijing (Peking) to about 51°N on Sakhalin and the Kuril islands in the USSR and around 55°N on the river Uda in far-eastern Russia. Between these extremes mandarin once bred in North Korea; in the Kirin Forest — another important centre — north of Antung in Manchuria, and throughout the watersheds of the Amur and Ussuri rivers (where they were first seen breeding by a European, Leopold von Schrenck, between 1853 and 1857); on the Japanese islands of Kyushu (mainly at Isahaya east of Nagasaki), Honshu (principally on Lake Ashi near Tokyo at about 36°N and at between 600 and 900

2. *Two mandarin drakes.*

3. *A mandarin drake in partial eclipse plumage.*

metres (2000-3000 feet) around Mount Fuji) and Hokkaido. Today, their breeding range in the USSR is in eastern Siberia, centred on the valleys of the Amur and Ussuri rivers; in China, mandarin breed locally in the north-east in Heilungkiang and eastern Kurin, and perhaps still in Hopeh. The main Japanese breeding population is on the island of Hokkaido.

MIGRATION

Between late August and early November mandarins in the USSR Maritime Territories, Manchuria and Hopeh province in northern China migrate south (some via Korea) to winter quarters in lowland south-eastern China, mainly south of the Chang Chiang (Yangtze Kiang) river, from around 23°N in Kwangtung province to approximately 27-29°N in Kiangsi and Chekiang provinces; they return north, already paired, between late March and early May. On the main Japanese islands there is a tendency to southwards dispersal in autumn.

Elsewhere in the Far East, mandarin have been recorded as far west as Mongolia, in Upper Assam and Manipur in eastern India, in the Japanese Ryukyu Reto archipelago, in Hong Kong and on Taiwan.

HABITAT

In contrast to most other Palearctic wildfowl, the mandarin is a bird of the middle-latitude temperate deciduous broad-leafed forest zone, where it frequents slow-flowing or standing fresh waters, with a dense growth of marginal trees and shrubs — especially where these overhang the water's edge to provide good cover, and where there is an abundance of reeds, sedges or other emergent vegetation. Although principally a lowland species, the mandarin also occurs in forested uplands and valleys to an altitude of 1500 metres (5000 feet), where it is found on small ponds as well as lakes, streams and rivers with well wooded islets. Mandarin are also occasionally seen on open waters (including the sea close to the coast) and land (especially cornfields and rice paddies) which

they visit to feed. They require plenty of arboreal or scrub cover for concealment and if alarmed take readily to the air, being well able to rise steeply and fast from confined places and dense cover. They nest in hollow tree stumps, holes in mature trees, fallen logs and even occasionally, it is said, among roots at or near ground level. Although usually shy and secretive, they readily accept human presence if left undisturbed.

FOOD AND FEEDING

In the Far East in spring mandarins eat insects (especially beetles), land snails, the seeds of wild grape *(Vitis* species), horsetail *(Equisetum* species), acorns *(Quercus* species), rice *(Oryza sativa)*, grasses (Gramineae) and fish, including minnows *(Phoxinus phoxinus)*, the young of lampreys (Petromyzonidae) and dead fish spawn. Water snails, worms and frogs are also sometimes taken. In August and September flocks raid fields of rice and buckwheat *(Fagopyrum esculentum)*; in early autumn land snails feature prominently in the birds' diet, and in later autumn and winter acorns become increasingly important.

POPULATION

The future of the mandarin in its native range in the Far East, where it is declining everywhere and where the surviving population is much fragmented, is extremely precarious. After the First World War it appeared to be rapidly becoming extinct, largely because of the loss of habitat due to the deforestation of its two main breeding grounds, the Tung Ling and Kirin Forests, which preceded human settlement after the Manchu emperors were deposed in 1911. This deforestation, which was completed by 1928, was carried out by the Chinese Republic following the policy of the Soviet Union in making Manchuria economically and agriculturally self-supporting, with heavy industrial areas and collective farms. Although loss of habitat through deforestation and subsequent development for human settlement is undoubtedly the main reason for the mandarin's decline in China (and in Japan), predatory animals of the cat tribe are numerous in the former country and birds of prey such as black kites *(Milvus migrans)* also take a toll of the mandarin population. On the other hand, the Chinese do not willingly kill mandarin, since for some 2500 years they have looked on the little ducks with admiration and respect as a symbol of love, conjugal fidelity and true happiness, and in any case mandarins, being rather dirty feeders, are not good to eat. Large numbers have been exported from China in the past, but a ban on their exportation was imposed by the Peoples' Republic in 1975.

Information on populations of mandarin in the Far East is scanty and hard to come by. In Japan there are believed to be fewer than 7000 individuals, in China between 500 and 1000 pairs, in Korea perhaps 300 individuals and in the USSR between 750 and 800 pairs. (A published figure of 8000 pairs given for the USSR is based on an extrapolation of fragmentary information and is certainly an extravagant over-estimation.) The total Far East population thus probably lies somewhere between 9800 and 10,900 individuals. This makes the mandarin a candidate for inclusion in the *Bird Red Data Book* of threatened birds of the world and also places great importance on the flourishing British population for the conservation of the species.

Naturalisation in Britain and elsewhere

The mandarin duck was first introduced to Britain shortly before 1745, when a drawing of *La Sarcelle de la Chine* ('The Chinese Teal'), as it was called, in the gardens of Sir Matthew Decker, Bt (a director of the East India Company), at Richmond Green in Surrey, was made by George Edwards for his *Natural History of Birds*. Edwards quotes from *History of Japan* (1727) by the Dutchman Engelbrecht Kaempfer, one of the earliest

Europeans to visit that country: 'Of ducks there are several different kinds, and as tame as the geese. One kind particularly I cannot forebear mentioning, because of the surprising beauty of its male, call'd *Kinmodsui*, which is so great, that being shewed its picture in colours, I could hardly believe my own eyes' — a delightful and apt description.

In 1830 two pairs of mandarins were purchased for the then considerable sum of £70 by the recently formed Zoological Society of London, in whose grounds they bred for the first time in Britain four years later, and where a male and female were drawn from life by John Gould for his *Birds of Asia* (1850).

The first recorded specimen of a mandarin in the wild in Britain was shot near the Thames at Cookham in Berkshire in May, 1866.

In the early years of the twentieth century the eleventh Duke of Bedford introduced some mandarin to his collection of waterfowl at Woburn Park in Bedfordshire, where they quickly settled down. By the outbreak of the First World War they numbered over three hundred, but because of the difficulty of feeding the birds in wartime the population shrank by half; a similar decline occurred during the Second World War.

In the years immediately preceding the First World War, Sir Richard Graham, Bt, of Netherby on the Border Esk in Cumberland (now Cumbria), obtained some mandarin from the Wormald and McLean game farm in East Anglia (to which they had been imported direct from the market at Canton in China), where they were artificially reared. Many of these birds failed to breed because, it was believed, the Chinese caponised them to protect their trade. A few, however, did breed successfully at Netherby and along the Esk for a number of years, but they did not spread into Scotland and elsewhere as had been hoped, and by about 1920 this population had died out.

In 1918 Viscount Grey of Fallodon added some mandarin bred by Wormald and McLean to his bird sanctuary in Northumberland; they thrived and spread widely throughout the surrounding countryside, and it was believed that

4. *Typical mandarin habitat at Virginia Water.*

they would eventually become firmly established. Lord Grey developed an extraordinary rapport with his birds — the author has in his possession a pencil drawing by J. C. Harrison of a mandarin drake perched on Lord Grey's hat (see also Gordon, 1937, and Savage, 1952, plate XVI). Unfortunately, after Lord Grey's death in 1933 the sanctuary survived for only a short time, and the mandarin eventually disappeared.

Between 1910 and 1935 Lieutenant-Colonel E. G. B. Meade-Waldo maintained a flock of free-flying mandarin at Stonewall Park near Edenbridge in Kent, where, probably because of the unsuitable habitat, the birds failed to become established.

The next avicultural collection in Britain to contain mandarin belonged to Alfred Ezra of Foxwarren Park near Cobham in Surrey, who in 1928 was presented with four or five pairs by the distinguished French ornithologist Jean Delacour. They bred in the following year and soon spread outside the park, eventually forming a discrete population which has been most successful, and from which mandarin dispersed by the mid 1970s south-west through Surrey to beyond Haslemere, northwards into Buckinghamshire and Middlesex, east and west to beyond Staines and Reading respectively, and south to the Surrey-Sussex border.

In January 1930 Ezra, with the help of J. Spedan Lewis and W. H. St Quintin, made an attempt to establish free-flying mandarin in some London parks. 99 full-winged birds imported from China were set free in Regent's Park, the central and Greenwich parks, but none, however, appears to have remained for very long; two leg-ringed individuals were subsequently traced to Hungary and one to Sweden. (Another remarkable example of the mandarin duck's powers of flight was provided by a pair which had been reared and ringed at Ekeberg, Norway, in 1962. These birds left Ekeberg at midday on 8th November and were shot at Seaton Burn in Northumberland at 5pm on the following day, having travelled a distance of 900 km, 560 miles, in 29 hours, at an average speed of 31 km/h, 19.3 mph.) A further fifteen (pinioned) pairs were released in Regent's Park in 1931, but a year later only a few remained (the others presumably having been killed by predators), and it was clear that the experiment had failed.

The mandarin at Virginia Water on the Surrey-Berkshire border, on which is based the largest population in Britain, that in Windsor Great Park, are presumed to be the descendants of Ezra's original stock at Foxwarren that found their way up the Bourne (where they were first seen in 1929 or 1930), a small stream that flows from Virginia Water into the Thames at Chertsey; they were probably supplemented by dispersants from earlier releases at Hampton Court and in inner London. By the early or mid 1930s they were well established and have been steadily increasing ever since. They have spread to virtually all the ponds throughout Windsor Great Park and Windsor Forest, in which they have found an ideal habitat, and in particular

frequent Great Meadow, Johnson's, Cow and Obelisk Ponds, and Sunninghill Park Lake. On waters adjacent to Windsor Park they occur at, among others, Titness Park near Sunninghill, where in winter there are sometimes in excess of one hundred, Bagshot Park, Ascot Place, Englemere Lodge (Ascot), and Foliejon Park (Winkfield). The population in Windsor Great Park is the largest and most successful in Britain, and it is to them that we must look for the future expansion of the species in the country.

In 1935 Ronald and Noel Stevens added some free-flying mandarin to their waterfowl collection at Walcot Hall in Shropshire, where at first they refused to breed because jackdaws (Corvus monedula) appropriated most of the suitable nesting sites — a problem that Andrew Davies, in his extensive study of the mandarin duck in Britain, has encountered with nesting boxes in Windsor Park. Once the jackdaws at Walcot had been disposed of, the mandarin began to breed freely, and by the outbreak of war in 1939 the population numbered about a

5. *A pair of mandarin at a nesting box in water.*

hundred. After Walcot was requisitioned during the war, when it was no longer possible to feed them, the mandarin dispersed as far west as North Wales and northwards to Lancashire. Since the war other free-flying populations have been formed in various parts of Britain, particularly in south-east, southern central and parts of the Midland counties of England and on the river Tay in Perthshire and Eye Water in Berwickshire.

The populations on the Tay and Eye Water are of special interest, being so far removed from any other established centres of free-flying birds, and the only large ones in Scotland. The former originates from a collection started by Mr J. Christie Laidlay at Holmwood on the outskirts of the city of Perth in 1946-7. In 1962 and 1963 half a dozen juvenile mandarin were feather-clipped to keep them at Holmwood for their first breeding season. By 1964 the population numbered only between six and ten individuals; by 1965 it had increased to at least seventeen; by 1973 it numbered between thirty and forty and had reached around double that number by 1975. The majority breed in some of the fifty or so nesting boxes set up on the trees in the garden, and several have been rescued from chimneys in their search for nesting sites. Mandarin from the Tay have nested successfully at Bonhard, Murrayshall and Scone Palace and have been reported at Methven Castle, Glencarse, Dunbog and near Newburgh in Fife, all within a radius of about 19 km (12 miles) of Holmwood. In the 1980s up to one hundred birds were counted in autumn and winter flocks on the Tay in the vicinity of Holmwood. The population on the Eye Water dates from the early 1970s and numbers around half that on the Tay.

Since the 1960s there has been some expansion of range of mandarin in the Windsor Great Park area into other parts of Surrey and Berkshire, as well as into Buckinghamshire and Middlesex. By 1969, when a census of the area was carried out, between 110 and 120 mandarin had colonised parts of the middle reaches of the river Mole and suitable neighbouring habitats. Mandarin in Middlesex are believed to be partly derived from the descendants of an avi-cultural collection started by Basil and Jack D'Eath at Monken Hadley in Hertfordshire in about 1930; in around 1960 a number of mandarin were allowed to fly free from Monken Hadley, and their progeny became established in the neighbourhood, where the population was annually augmented by further releases.

In about 1972-3 a small number of mandarin became established at Leonardslee near Horsham in West Sussex, the home of Sir Giles Loder, Bt, where a minor population was formed.

UNITED STATES

Since about 1977, a free-flying population of mandarin has been established north of San Francisco in northern California, where the birds live in an area of rough, rolling, heavily wooded hills some 50 km (30 miles) inland from the coast. The habitat and climate of this region seem as suitable for mandarins as they are for wood ducks, which are native to and plentiful in this area. The two species share thirty or more nesting boxes on one large lake, and a similar number on outlying ponds, although the mandarin invariably select the best sites. Since the mandarin are fed throughout the year on the main lake, and in the breeding season also on the smaller ponds, they cannot be regarded as living entirely naturally, as such artificial management alters their normal behaviour pattern and creates an unnaturally high population density.

In 1987 the total mandarin population in this area was estimated at around 550. The birds have been sighted up to 50 km away from the nesting lake, and nest-boxes have been erected in some of these localities to try to persuade them to extend their current range. Their principal predators in California are large-mouth bass *(Micropterus salmoides)*, bobcats *(Felis rufus)*, raccoons *(Procyon lotor)*, American bullfrogs *(Rana catesbeiana)*, owls and hawks.

WEST GERMANY

In November 1987 25 pairs of mandarins were counted on the lake in the Charlottenburg Gardens in West Berlin, suggesting the presence of an established population.

The mandarin's year

The mandarin's year can be said to begin around late September, when, a few weeks after most of the adult males have emerged from their sombre eclipse plumage into which they moulted during the summer and have resumed their full breeding finery, the birds start to form large autumnal flocks.

COURTSHIP

It is at about this time that communal courtship commences, and the adult drakes begin their elaborate and complex display routines. These take place largely in the early morning and evening and involve several males and one or more females. They consist mainly of recurrent threats and pursuits between males, and short bursts of bill-flicking. The drakes assume a 'full-sail' or 'courtship-intent' posture with raised occipital crest and frequently utter a short 'prfruib' call with the neck stretched vertically upwards. Secondary displays include a 'display-shake', in which the male lowers and then rapidly jerks his head upwards while violently shaking his head and tail and uttering a soft whirring whistle, and a 'double display-shake', where the male dips his bill in the water, shakes his head while uttering a short wheezy whistle, and finally quickly and sharply dips his head and shakes again before pushing his neck upwards, while repeating his call and energetically twitching his tail (Cramp and Simmons, 1977).

These communal courtship rituals continue intermittently throughout the autumn and winter months until the flocks break up and, normally by about February, pair formation, in which the female is believed to play the leading role, is complete. This is indicated principally by the female directing an 'inciting display' at her rejected suitors; unilateral and reciprocal mutual preening; the drake dipping his head and bill towards the duck and then drawing his bill down his own breast or flank; the pursuit of one sex by the other; ceremonial synchronised drinking; and preening behind the wing by the male. Mandarin are normally monogamous (sometimes over several breeding seasons) though some males may be bigamous or even occasionally promiscuous.

A change of sex can occur in many birds, but in the case of the mandarin duck it is especially obvious because of the elaborate plumage of the male, which is suppressed by female hormones. In the females of most birds only the left ovary is functional; if it becomes damaged in any way (for example by being shot) the rudimentary right ovary sometimes increases in size and acts, not as an ovary, but as a testis, resulting in a change of sex.

NESTING

During February the flocks that assembled in autumn and remained together throughout the winter begin to break up and disperse, as paired birds seek a suitable nesting site. This, selected by the female, is almost invariably in a hole or cavity in the trunk or a branch of a tree (especially oaks, *Quercus* species), up to 2.5 metres (8 feet) in depth and from ground level to a height of 15 metres (50 feet). Nests are said to have been found very occasionally on the ground in thick vegetation, under a bush or fallen branch or among tree roots. Nesting boxes are readily accepted in those areas where woodland management has reduced the amount of mature standing timber. Nests are located according to the availability of suitable sites. The nest itself is a simple depression lined with down.

The first eggs may be laid as early as late March, but the main laying period lasts from early April to the end of May. The nine to twelve off-white eggs, measuring about 51 by 37 mm (2 by 1½ inches) are laid almost daily. Incubation, by the female only, lasts for between 28 and 33 days and begins shortly before the laying of the final egg. The drake, who normally stays nearby during incubation and even occasionally enters the nest hole

6. *A mandarin duck and drake in pre-copulatory display.*

7. *A mandarin female in sex-change plumage.*

8. *A mandarin female at a nest-hole in a tree.*

9. *A mandarin duck, drake and ducklings.*

and remains with the female for several hours, accompanies his mate when she leaves the nest — usually at dawn and dusk — to feed. This may involve a return flight of up to 3.25 km (2 miles). During early incubation, the female may take a third feeding break in the afternoon. Not infrequently, two or more females may lay a total of up to 34 eggs in the same nest ('dumping').

Dumping is a phenomenon which occurs in many species of birds. With mandarin, up to four or more females may dump eggs in the same nest, which will then normally be 'adopted' and incubated by a single female, while the other females start to lay again elsewhere. Some females seem to be parasitic, laying eggs but never incubating them. If the number of dumped eggs is more than around thirty, those on the periphery may get cold, in which case the nest will probably be abandoned; from one clutch of 32 eggs, however, 22 ducklings left the nest, and several more eggs hatched but the ducklings later died. If a clutch of dumped eggs numbers no more than about twenty, all will usually hatch successfully.

In a normal clutch the eggs hatch at around the same time. The young emerge well developed and usually leave the nest and its vicinity within 24 hours. The female stands at the base of the tree with her body upright and her head pointing upwards, uttering a soft encouraging call to her offspring which, according to Savage (1952), is not used at any other time of the year. Unlike ducklings of ground-nesting species, mandarin nestlings show no fear of heights in joining their mother; they scramble up the sides of the nest with their needle-sharp claws and then, protected by their light weight and thick down, gently drop to the ground, where, under their mother's guidance, they may travel for several kilometres to find water and to feed. The upperparts of ducklings are dark brown, the underparts a buff or greyish white. The eye, which is dark brown, is unusually large, and there is a dark brown stripe running from behind it to the neck, with another less distinct one underneath behind the ear coverts, the two framing a white stripe which corresponds to that in the adult female. The edge of the wing is pale buff, with two indistinct bars of the same colour on the sides. Fledging takes from 40 to 45 days, and the young become increasingly independent of their parents shortly afterwards.

While mandarin ducklings are small much of their time is spent on land; this may save them from being eaten by pike (Esox lucius), a fate that befalls the young of many waterbirds. On land, their principal predators are probably carrion crows (Corvus corone corone) and magpies (Pica pica). If danger threatens on land or in the water or if she is flushed from her nest in late incubation, the female mandarin shows great courage in protecting her brood; after giving a throaty 'rrrruck' alarm call, she will attempt to distract an intruder by feigning an injury such as a broken wing.

On the other hand, mandarin females often spend considerable periods of time away from their young, leaving them to fend for themselves; the ducklings are often to be found feeding alone quite unconcernedly in waterside undergrowth. If disturbed on land, they either 'freeze' or jump quickly into the water, where they swim submerged for up to 15 metres (50 feet) before surfacing, when they patter rapidly along the surface with swiftly beating wings, uttering a shrill peeping cry. Ducklings also have a piping contact call with the female, which carries for a considerable distance. Some occasionally stray from their siblings and become 'explorers', usually surviving quite well on their own. The survival rate of ducklings is usually between three and five out of clutches of nine to twelve eggs.

MOULTING

While the ducks are busy rearing their broods, the drakes form all-male gatherings during the first half of May, where from early June they slowly moult out of their gorgeous breeding plumage into the dull eclipse plumage — very similar to that of the females — previously described. For a time, after the primary wing feathers have been shed, they are unable to fly. During this period they are particularly susceptible to attack from aquatic and terrestrial predators. By late September most of the males have regained their former glory, although some do not reassume their full winter plumage until as late as November. The females, being occupied in rearing their young, moult some four weeks later than their mates and so have a correspondingly later period of flightlessness.

By the end of September, when the young of the year have become fully independent, mandarin begin to gather again into large autumnal flocks. By early October the first communal courtship rituals have begun, and the mandarin's year has come full circle.

The mandarin in Britain

The haunts of mandarin in Britain are much the same as those in the Far East — secluded rivers, streams, ponds and freshwater lakes surrounded by mature deciduous woodland, especially those with a wealth of rhododendron *(Rhododendron ponticum)* undergrowth. They are occasionally seen on open waters but feed, both in and out of the water, along wooded or shrub-covered margins. Although in their native range mandarin are both migratory and dispersive, in Britain there is only some relatively local seasonal movement.

DISTRIBUTION

In 1928 a very large consignment of crated mandarin ducks arrived in Paris from Hong Kong; the birds, many of them dead or dying, were acquired by Jean Delacour, who managed to save some 45, from which he selected four or five pairs to give to his friend Alfred Ezra. Ezra released them on his estate at Foxwarren Park near Cobham, Surrey, where they bred freely, and their descendants — possibly augmented by some of those freed in the London parks in 1930 — soon began to spread and disperse outside Foxwarren and eventually formed, in Surrey and east Berkshire, by far the most important population of wild mandarins in Britain.

Their success is attributed firstly to the fact that they were released into an ideal habitat, with plenty of streams and large and small sheets of water, a profusion of rhododendron and other marginal undergrowth for shelter, and mature open deciduous woodland, especially oak, chestnut and beech trees to provide an abundant choice of nesting sites and autumn and winter feeding; and secondly because the founder stock was composed of individuals chosen from the survivors of the shipment from Hong Kong, which were themselves the survivors of a much larger number originally caught in their winter quarters in southern China and were thus inherently the strongest and — coming originally from northern China and the USSR — were derived from a wide genetic base.

The map reproduced from *The Atlas of Breeding Birds in Britain and Ireland* shows what was believed to be the distribution of mandarin ducks in Britain in 1976. Most colonies were associated

10. *Map showing breeding distribution of mandarin ducks in Britain in 1976. (From 'The Atlas of Breeding Birds in Britain and Ireland', compiled by J. T. R. Sharrock, British Trust for Ornithology, 1976.)*

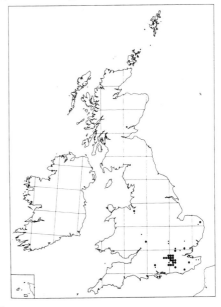

11. Left: *A man-darin duck emerging from her nest-hole.*

12. Below: *A man-darin female at a nesting box on a tree.*

13. *A group of mandarins standing on ice.*

with, or dependent upon, neighbouring collections of waterfowl such as those at Leckford (Hampshire), Leeds Castle (Kent), Tillingbourne Manor (Surrey), Bassmead, Apethorpe Lake and Milton Park (all now in Cambridgeshire), Monken Hadley (Hertfordshire) — which is known to have been the source of mandarin breeding in the wild in northern Middlesex — Salhouse (Norfolk), Eaton Hall (Cheshire) and Holmwood on the river Tay on the outskirts of Perth. A formerly flourishing colony on the Duke of Bedford's Woburn Abbey estate in Bedfordshire was found to have declined.

Most of the sites at which mandarin have been recorded in Britain are in south-east England, especially east Berkshire, Surrey and southern Buckinghamshire. Although observations of birds during the breeding season are mostly on or near inland fresh waters, small numbers occur from time to time on the coast.

The map taken from *The Atlas of Wintering Birds in Britain and Ireland* (1986) purports to show the seasonal alteration in the distribution of mandarin in Britain compared to that depicted in *The Atlas of Breeding Birds*, and also the extent to which the species was thought

14. *Map showing winter distribution of mandarin ducks in Britain in 1986. (From 'The Atlas of Wintering Birds in Britain and Ireland', compiled by Peter Lack, T. and A. D. Poyser, 1986.)*

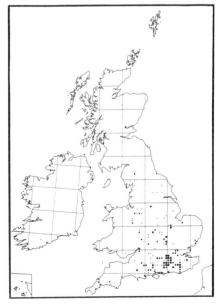

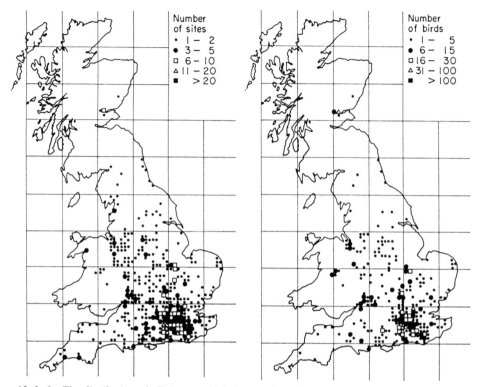

15. Left: *The distribution of all sites at which the mandarin duck has been recorded in the wild between 1745 and 1987. (From 'Distribution and Status of the Mandarin Duck in Britain', by A. K. Davies, Bird Study, 35 (1988), 204.)*

16. Right: *The distribution of all records of mandarin ducks during the breeding season (March-June) between 1970 and 1987. (From 'Distribution and Status of the Mandarin Duck in Britain', by A. K. Davies, Bird Study, 35 (1988), 204.)*

to have extended its range during the decade. Davies (1988), however, believes there is little evidence for a material alteration in the range of the mandarin in Britain during the last sixty years, nor any evidence of a substantial seasonal change, although in central Surrey, and to some extent elsewhere, mandarin disperse from their breeding areas in late summer and do not return to them until the following spring. Davies's map indicates that mandarin have probably always been far more widespread than the two *Atlas* maps and previous accounts (including the present author's of 1977) have suggested. This is almost certainly the result of under-recording due to the mandarin's shy and secretive nature,

although a few new colonies have probably arisen as a result of escapes or deliberate releases from avicultural collections, such as that based on a man-made lake at Dofor, near Newtown, Powys, in central Wales. From time to time mandarin have been reported from the Isle of Wight in the south northwards to Loch Lomond in Scotland.

POPULATION

For the same reason, figures for the total population of mandarin ducks in Britain have most likely always been underestimates. Savage (1952) put the total at over 500 individuals; since then, published totals and dates have been as follows: 200 pairs (1967); 250+ pairs

18

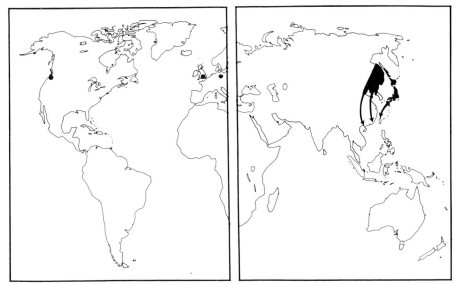

17. *Maps showing (left) naturalised and (right) natural distribution of the mandarin duck. (From 'Naturalized Birds of the World' by Christopher Lever, Longman, 1987).*

(1972); 300-400 pairs (1976); 1000 individuals (1977); 850-1000 pairs (1986); 3500-5000 birds (1987).

Most estimates of the total numbers of mandarins based on sightings are probably unreliable, mainly as a result of the behaviour of the birds and their choice of habitat. Mandarin are wary birds and show a preference for secluded, undisturbed and often private waters, where they are adept at slipping quietly away before being seen.

Based on the percentage of recaptured birds from a total of over 500 ringed on a private lake in Windsor Park over a two-year period in the mid 1980s, Davies has estimated the total British population of mandarins to be at least 7000 individuals. This is well in excess of the previous highest published estimate and is between 64 and 71 per cent of the total Far East population.

There seem to be three principal reasons for the successful establishment of the mandarin duck in Britain: firstly, the existence of a vacant ecological niche for a perching duck that eats mainly nuts in autumn and winter and nests almost exclusively in holes in trees; secondly, the

presence of suitable habitats, exemplified by that in Windsor Great Park; and thirdly, the abandonment of the instinct to migrate — an important feature in the successful naturalisation of alien birds, and one of the reasons why the Canada goose *(Branta canadensis)* is now a familiar sight in many parts of Britain. The mandarin's main limiting factors seem to be the availability of suitable nesting sites (since it competes with several hole-nesting native birds, and even with alien grey squirrels, *Sciurus carolinensis*), and the amount of acceptable habitats.

The population of wild mandarin ducks in Britain now almost certainly exceeds the whole of that in the Far East outside Japan and probably equals the total in that country. The conservation importance, in a world context, of British mandarins cannot, therefore, be over-emphasised. In recent years Père David's deer *(Elaphurus davidianus)* has been successfully reintroduced from England to its native range in China; perhaps before long mandarin ducks from Britain will be the subject of a similar reintroduction to the People's Republic.

18. *A Japanese porcelain jar with mandarins on rockwork underneath prunus branches and various flowers: Arita, Fukugawa kiln, nineteenth century.*

The mandarin in oriental literature and art

The mandarin duck, known in China as *yüan yang* and in Japan as *oshidori*, reputedly received its name, by analogy, from seventeenth-century English merchants out of their appreciation of its superiority over others of its kind, implied in the title 'mandarin' (in Chinese *kwan* or *kwūn*), a public official, counsellor or minister of state. During the period of the Ching Dynasty (1644-1912), the 'mandarin' language was the Chinese employed in official and legal circles, and a mandarin drake was the emblem of the seventh grade of civilian mandarin officials.

Since around 200 BC the mandarin duck has been revered by the Buddhists of China and Japan for the beauty of its plumage and for its behaviour and, being normally monogamous, it has for long been regarded as a symbol and example to mankind of connubial bliss, fidelity and mutual affection: this is shown by the many appearances it makes in Chinese and Japanese literature and art from the sixth century BC onwards. The mandarin was for hundreds of years a protected bird in China and Japan, which it was unlucky, if not illegal, to destroy.

LITERATURE

The earliest references to the mandarin in oriental literature occur in the writings of the disciples of the Chinese philosopher Confucius (551-478 BC), of which Savage (1952) quotes the following example: 'There are mandarin ducks on the dam, folding their left wings. Long life to our Lord, well may blessing for ever be his.' The folding of the left wing portends 'blessing heaped upon blessing'.

A legend, known to the Japanese as Buddha Ohmu Kyō, tells of a pair of mandarin foretelling the coming of the Lord. As a child, Siddartha Gautama (Buddha, 'The Great Enlightened One'), born *c.*507 BC, is said to have had a pair of mandarin as pets, which so impressed him by their behaviour and display of mutual affection that in later years he made numerous references to them in his teaching. Another legend relates that Amida Buddha from time to time assumed the form of a mandarin to lend emphasis to his preaching.

Savage quotes three examples of references to the mandarin in the literature of the T'ang Dynasty (AD 620-900). In *The Beautiful Women* by Tu Fu occur the following lines: 'My husband holds me in light esteem, but his new mistress seems as beautiful as jade . . . the mandarin duck and drake do not roost apart, but wrapt in his new favourite's smiles, how can he hear his old love's sighs?'

From *The Song of Never-ending Grief* by Po Chu-I come the lines: 'The mandarin duck and drake tiles glitter coldly in the hoar frost, the Emperor is cold beneath the kingfisher quilt, for who is there to share it with him?' Referring to this poem, Savage points out that, if a Chinese wants to refer to a double or pair of anything, he associates it with the mandarin duck: thus, for example, there is a mandarin duck double pillow, a mandarin duck double bed-cover and a mandarin duck sword with a pair of blades emerging from a single handle.

The following lines are taken from *A Song of Chaste Women* by Mêng Chiao: 'The mandarin duck and drake pair for life, even so the chaste woman prides herself on following her husband to the tomb, and throws away her life.'

On the same general theme, a Japanese legend tells of a falconer named Sanjō who killed a mandarin drake, whose mate, however, escaped. That night Sanjō dreamed that a beautiful but sad and accusing woman appeared before him. The following day the female mandarin flew up to him and with her bill tore open her breast at his feet. Sanjō, the legend concludes, was so overcome with remorse that he thereupon became a monk.

19. *A pair of mid nineteenth-century Japanese gold lacquer boxes in the form of mandarin ducks.*

ART

'A picture', say the Chinese, 'is a voiceless poem', meaning that paintings are not intended to be strictly representational but rather suggestive of a poetical idea; this is certainly true in most oriental paintings of mandarin ducks, which tend to emphasise the theme of beauty and love at the expense of strict anatomical accuracy.

The earliest representations of mandarin in Chinese painting date from the period of the Sung Dynasty (AD 960 to c.1279). An early example is a fine pen and ink drawing of a pair of mandarin beneath a rock and a sunflower, by Tsao Chung (Chao Chung), known to the Japanese as Chō-shō; this delicate drawing carries the seal of the collection of Emperor Kao Tsung and his inscription 'Marvellous pen of Tsao Chung'. In the library of Cambridge University is a long scroll dating from the Ming Dynasty (1368-1644) painted around 1430 by Li-y-ho, showing in part a pair of mandarin

swimming beneath a tree peony, the emblem of spring, love and feminine charm.

The British Museum possesses two particularly fine paintings of mandarin. The earlier one, painted on silk by Naorubu Sōhyei (1519-92; Kano School), shows a waterfall plunging through a cloud into a mist-enshrouded stream which tumbles through a rocky gorge overhung by maple trees; a female mandarin in the water gazes up at her mate, who is standing on a rock beneath a peony. The later picture, depicting a pair of mandarin swimming side by side under snow-laden plum blossom — an emblem of winter — was painted in the seventeenth century by Murata Sohaku. The composition of this picture is remarkably similar to that of Li-y-ho.

In the early eighteenth century the art of printmaking was introduced to Japan from Europe and several examples of this form of art depicting mandarin ducks can be seen in the Victoria and Albert

22

Museum in London. One, by Koriusai (c.1733), shows a pair swimming together among reeds with snow-clad mountains in the background; in another, a fan-print by Kitao Shigemasa (1738-1819), a female mandarin in a stream gazes up at her mate standing on a flat rock underneath a peony, a somewhat similar composition to the silk painting by Naorubu Sōhyei; in a third, an illustration from the *Sketchbook of Birds and Animals* by Fukuzensai Kagen (1741-86), a pair of mandarin, the duck more naturalistically shown than in the two previous examples, are shown swimming beneath the branch of a peony. Hiroshige (1796-1858) produced many magnificent examples of the printmaker's art that included mandarin, the most frequently reproduced being one showing a pair displaying to one another under a *fuyo*, a variety of rose-mallow.

As in painting, so in pottery and porcelain the earliest representations of mandarin date from the Sung Dynasty; the Victoria and Albert Museum and the British Museum possess several fine examples of translucent Ting ware of this period decorated with mandarin. A number of pieces of delicate Chinese embroidery from the Kien Lung period, mostly depicting mandarin swimming among reeds with peonies overhead, can be seen in the former museum.

Mandarin are also well represented in the field of Japanese and Chinese sculpture, appearing, frequently in pairs, in a variety of materials such as rose quartz, ivory, jade, lacquer, gold and bronze. One of the finest known examples of the mandarin in Chinese art, a magnificent bronze of a drake entwined with snakes, of the Western Han Dynasty and dating from the second or first century BC, was excavated at Shi-chai-shan in Yünnan province in south-western China in 1955. The locality where this item was discovered is several hundred kilometres away from the nearest current range of the mandarin duck in China.

ACKNOWLEDGEMENTS
For their comments on the text my thanks are due to Mr Andrew Davies, Dr Janet Kear of the Wildfowl and Wetlands Trust, and Mr Lawton L. Shurtleff of the United States. For information on the size of populations in the Far East I am indebted to Miss Alison Stattersfield of the International Council for Bird Preservation and Dr Hito Higuchi of the Wild Bird Society of Japan. I am also grateful to the British Trust for Ornithology, Dr David Parkin, editor of *Bird Study*, Blackwell Scientific Publications and Mr Davies for permission to reproduce the distribution maps.

Illustrations are acknowledged as follows: Blackwell Scientific Publications, 15, 16; J. B. Blossom, 3, 5, 6, 7, 9, 13; British Trust for Ornithology, 10; A. K. Davies, 4, 8, 12; Frank Lane Picture Agency, cover (R. Van Nostrand); Ichiro Kikuta, 11; Natural Science Photos, 2 (Richard Revels); T. and A. D. Poyser, 14; Wildfowl Trust, 1 (K. Portman); 17, 18 and 19 are by the author.

Places to visit

Mandarin ducks can be seen at the following centres managed by the Wildfowl and Wetlands Trust:

Arundel: Mill Road, Arundel, West Sussex BN18 9PB. Telephone: 0903 883355.
Martin Mere: Martin Mere, Burscough, Ormskirk, Lancashire L40 0TA. Telephone: 0704 895181.
Peakirk: Peakirk, Peterborough, Cambridgeshire PE6 7NP. Telephone: 0733 252271.
Slimbridge: Slimbridge, Gloucester GL2 7BT. Telephone: 0453 890333.
Washington: District 15, Washington, Tyne and Wear NE38 8LE. Telephone: 091 4165454.
Welney: Pintail House, Hundred Foot Bank, Welney, Wisbech, Cambridgeshire PE14 9TN. Telephone: 0353 860711.

Mandarin can also be seen in many private avicultural collections open to the public, such as the Pensthorpe Waterfowl Park, Fakenham, Norfolk NR21 0LN. Telephone: 0328 51465.

The best place to see mandarin ducks in the wild is Virginia Water, on the Berkshire/Surrey border in Windsor Great Park, on which is based the largest and most flourishing population of mandarin in Britain. Virginia Water lies at the southern end of Windsor Great Park. If coming from London, leave Staines on the A30 and turn right ¼ mile past the Wheatsheaf Hotel on to the A329. After one mile park in the public car park on the right. Mandarin can be found anywhere on the lake, especially north of the car park and at the eastern end, and, particularly in autumn and winter, also on Obelisk, Cow, Johnson's, Great Meadow and other ponds within the park.

Further reading

Beames, I. R. 'Welcome Immigrants', *International Wildlife*, 315-16, 1969.
Cramp, S., and Simmons, K. E. L. (editors). *The Birds of the Western Palearctic,* volume 1. Oxford University Press, 1977.
Davies, A. K. 'Mandarin Manoeuvres', *Wildlife*, 412-15, 1978.
Davies, A. K. 'The British Mandarins — Outstripping Their Ancestors', *BTO News,* 136 (1985), 12.
Davies, A. K. 'The Distribution and Status of the Mandarin Duck *Aix galericulata* in Britain', *Bird Study*, 35 (1988), 203-8.
Fitter, R. S. R. *The Ark in Our Midst.* Collins, 1959.
Gordon, S. *Edward Grey and His Birds.* Country Life, 1937.
Grey of Fallodon, Viscount. *The Charm of Birds.* Hodder and Stoughton, 1927.
Jackson, E. 'Mandarin Duck', in *Birds of the World*, part II, volume 1, 295. IPC, 1969.
Lack, P. (editor). *The Atlas of Wintering Birds in Britain and Ireland.* T. and A. D. Poyser, 1986.
Lever, C. 'The Mandarin Duck in Britain', *Country Life* 122 (1957), 829-31.
Lever, C. *The Naturalized Animals of the British Isles.* Hutchinson, 1977.
Lever, C. *Naturalized Birds of the World.* Longman, 1987.
Owen, M.; Atkinson-Willes, G. L. and Salmon, D. G. *Wildfowl in Great Britain.* Cambridge University Press, second edition, 1986.
Savage, C. *The Mandarin Duck.* A. and C. Black, 1952.
Sharrock, J. T. R. (editor). *The Atlas of Breeding Birds in Britain and Ireland.* British Trust for Ornithology, 1976.
Sowerby, A. *Nature in Chinese Art.* John Day, New York, 1940.